Back to Basics

ENGLISH

for 9–10 year olds

BOOK TWO

Sheila Lane and Marion Kemp

Alphabetical order

The words in a dictionary are arranged in **alphabetical order**.

Write the complete aphabet using capital letters.

A																									Z

When the words in a set begin with the **same** letter, look at the **second** letter of each word.

pat	pet	put
said	send	sold

Write each set of verbs in **alphabetical order**.

swing	_____	glare	_____	prowl	_____
skate	_____	grasp	_____	pace	_____
search	_____	gaze	_____	plod	_____

When the words in a set begin with the **same two letters**, look at the **third** letter of each word.

shake
show
shut

Write each set of words in **alphabetical order**.

wreck	_____	splendid	_____	knuckle	_____
write	_____	spell	_____	know	_____
wrap	_____	spring	_____	kneel	_____

Use your dictionary to find words, all beginning with **qu**, which mean:

1   an amount of something _____

2   a group of four _____

3   something which is asked _____

4   a line of people or vehicles _____

You will find these words
in a **mathematics** book: Use your dictionary to help you write their meanings.

area   ....

circle   ....

cube   ....

fraction ....

graph   ....

triangle ....

You will find these words
in a **science** book: Use your dictionary to help you write their meanings.

diagram   ....

fossil   ....

liquid   ....

magnet   ....

planet   ....

solid   ....

Challenge

In this alphabet code each letter is moved along **one** place.

a	b	c	d	e	f	g	h	i	j	k	l	m	n	o	p	q	r	s	t	u	v	w	x	y	z	a
	a	b	c	d	e	f	g	h	i	j	k	l	m	n	o	p	q	r	s	t	u	v	w	x	y	z

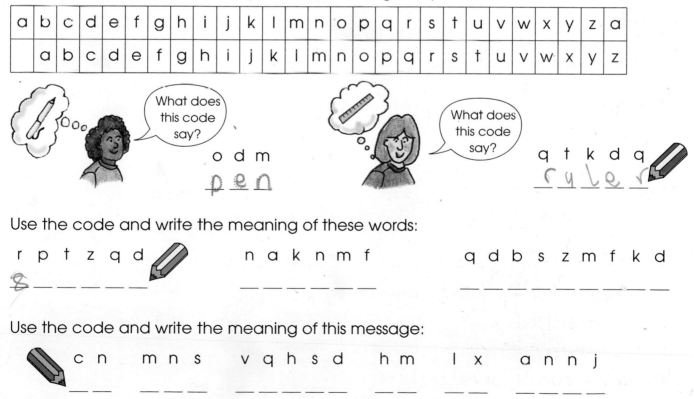

What does this code say?

o d m
_p e n_

What does this code say?

q t k d q
_r u l e r_

Use the code and write the meaning of these words:

r p t z q d   n a k n m f   q d b s z m f k d

_s_ _ _ _ _ _   _ _ _ _ _ _   _ _ _ _ _ _ _ _ _

Use the code and write the meaning of this message:

c n   m n s   v q h s d   h m   l x   a n n j

_ _   _ _ _   _ _ _ _ _   _ _   _ _   _ _ _ _

Comprehension

Read about The Boy King

Edward VI was crowned King of England, in Westminster Abbey, when he was only nine years old. He was too young to reign on his own, so his uncle, the Duke of Somerset, ruled for him. The Duke was called the Lord Protector.

Edward was a quiet boy, but he enjoyed playing games with other boys. His favourite was a chasing game called Prison Bars. If Edward ever did anything wrong he was never punished. Instead, another boy, called Barnaby, was whipped in place of the King. Barnaby was called the King's Whipping Boy.

Young Edward learned Latin, Greek, French and mathematics. When he was fifteen years old he caught a chill, became ill and died in the year 1553. Many schools were built and named after him. One of these was King Edward VI Grammar School in Norwich.

Read the questions.

Put a tick under the correct answer.

1   Where was Edward VI crowned?

in St Paul's Cathedral	in Westminster Abbey	in Buckingham Palace
☐	☐	☐

2   How old was Edward when he became king?

twenty-one	fifteen	nine
☐	☐	☐

3   What was the Duke of Somerset called?

the Lord Protector	the Lord Projector	the Lord Prospector
☐	☐	☐

About the information

Read the questions.
Choose the best word, or group of words, to fit the information and put a (ring) round it.

1   Why did the Duke of Somerset rule for King Edward?

because Edward couldn't read   because Edward played games   because Edward was so young

2   What was Edward's favourite game?

chess   knucklestones   Prison Bars

3   How did Edward die?

in battle   in a fight with Barnaby   of a chill

How the story is written

Draw a (ring) round the best set of words for your answer.

1   The word **protect** means: to accuse   to complain   to keep safe

2   The word **reign** means: water drops from the sky   to rule   a strap used to guide a horse

Write **one** sentence to explain how Barnaby was important to King Edward.

....

Using your best joined up handwriting, copy this sentence on the lines.

When he was nine years old Edward learned Latin, Greek, French and mathematics.

....

....

Grammar

A **preposition** is a word that shows the relationship between **two** nouns or pronouns.

Ants live **under** the ground.

Ants
ground } . . . . nouns

under . . . . preposition

Read these examples of **prepositions**:

against	beneath	in	on	round
along	between	into	out	through
among	by	near	over	to
behind	from	off	past	under

Draw a (ring) round the **prepositions** in the zig-zag.

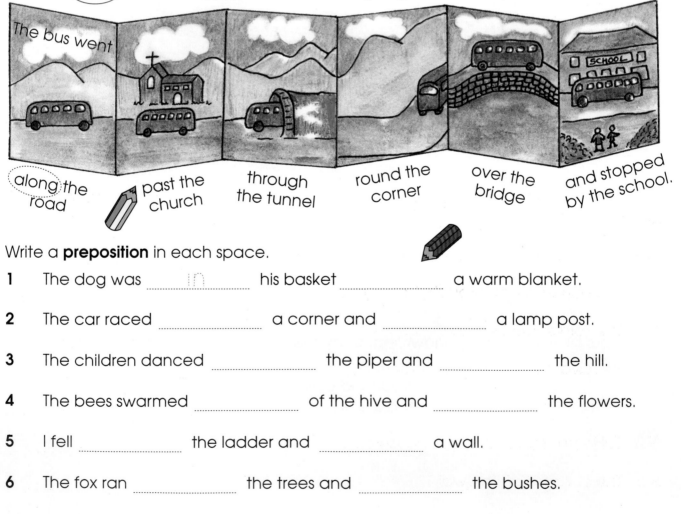

The bus went

along the road   past the church   through the tunnel   round the corner   over the bridge   and stopped by the school.

Write a **preposition** in each space.

1   The dog was _____ in _____ his basket _____ a warm blanket.

2   The car raced _____ a corner and _____ a lamp post.

3   The children danced _____ the piper and _____ the hill.

4   The bees swarmed _____ of the hive and _____ the flowers.

5   I fell _____ the ladder and _____ a wall.

6   The fox ran _____ the trees and _____ the bushes.

Write the **prepositions** in the box as **pairs of opposites**.

under	up
below	without
to	outside
before	off
down	from
with	over
after	above
on	inside

under and _over_ _____ and _____

_____ and _____ _____ and _____

_____ and _____ _____ and _____

_____ and _____ _____ and _____

Change the **prepositions** in each sentence to give it the **opposite** meaning.

e.g.   I went <u>up</u> the ladder.   I went <u>down</u> the ladder.

1   The cat ran inside the shed.   1   _____

2   A tram went over the bridge.   2   _____

3   My friend went after me.   3   _____

4   I forgot to turn on the light.   4   _____

5   Birds flew below the trees.   5   _____

Draw a (ring) round the **nouns** in each sentence.

Write the **preposition** in each sentence.

e.g. The (aeroplane) flew over the (town.)   _over_

1   The hunter crept through the bushes.   _____

2   The soldier ran behind a tank.   _____

3   Fish swam beneath the surface.   _____

4   Ahmet kicked a ball against the wall.   _____

5   Sukie put the apples into a basket.   _____

6   The child fell off the wall.   _____

Spelling

Draw a (ring) round the letter string (ight) in these words:

might   tightly   delighted   frightful   midnight

Draw a (ring) round the letter string (itch) in these words:

hitch   switched   witch   pitch   stitches

Read the words in the box.

garage	trio	triangle	unicorn
message	average	manage	triplet
uniform	lance	united	distance
balance	tripod	entrance	universe

Write the words in the box in **family** sets.

–age	–ance	uni–	tri–
....	....	....	....
....	....	....	....
....	....	....	....
....	....	....	....

LOOK	**SAY**	**COVER**	**WRITE**	**CHECK**
at each word	each word	each word	from memory	your spelling

light
witch
garage
lance
unicorn
triangle

An **anagram** is made by rearranging the letters in a word so that they make another word.

e.g.   could
        cloud

        inch
        chin

Rearrange the letters of each word in colour so that they make a word which fits the sentence. The clue is in the meaning of the sentence itself.

1   There are eleven players in a football mate.

2   The juicy cheap was quite delicious.

3   The master ran into a wide river.

4   I put butter and jam on my beard.

5   We laid the bleat ready for supper.

6   Our best pleat crashed to the floor.

Challenge

Make **families** of words, having four or more letters, from the word:

triangles

–ai–	–ing	–age	–ea–
train			

Making notes

Key words are words which are essential to the meaning of a sentence.

e.g.   Squirrels and beavers are both rodents.
Squirrels ~~and~~ beavers ~~are both~~ rodents.

The key words are: squirrels – beavers – rodents

Tick the important key words and cross out the unimportant words in each sentence.

Write the three key words here:

1   Penguins live in the Antarctic.

2   Whales live in the sea.

3   Flying-fish glide on their fins.

4   Some mosquitoes carry diseases.

5   The greenfly is a common insect.

6   Most snakes crawl along the ground.

7   A spider has eight legs.

8   A bat is a winged mammal.

Write a complete sentence for each set of key words.

honey
bees
pollen
collect

1 _____

robins   sparrows
pigeons   wings

2 _____

eggs
size   tortoise
tennis balls

3 _____

I'm playing notes on my pipe.

I'm making notes in my notebook.

I'm writing a note to your teacher.

Making notes helps you to remember important facts.
By finding **key words** you can write **useful notes**.

Tick the four key words and cross out the unimportant words in each sentence.

1   Monkeys, apes and humans are all primates.

2   A lizard can replace its lost tail.

3   The lion, the tiger and the leopard are all carnivorous.

4   Some insects and birds migrate in very long swarms.

5   Wolves and foxes both belong to the family of dogs.

6   The Australian kangaroo keeps its young in a pouch.

Write the four **key words** in the notebook.

1

2

3

4

5

6

Read each set of **notes**.

giraffe neck
high leaves
trees

claws eagles
seizing prey

nest squirrel
tree drey

Write **one** complete sentence for each set.

1

2

3

Punctuation

Write the correct punctuation at the end of each of the following:

1   How many in a dozen
2   What a good idea
3   Is that the answer
4   I think that it's ten
5   Don't ask me

6   How old are you
7   I am nine
8   Do as you're told
9   Why are you crying
10   Stand up

, One use of a **comma** is to separate words which come together in a list. There is **no comma** when **and** separates the last two words.

Punctuate these sentences correctly.

1   The Cam Dee Ure and Wye are all English rivers
2   Some capital cities of Europe are Paris Rome Oslo London and Berlin
3   Ayr Alva and Elie are Scottish towns
4   In the Mediterranean are the islands of Majorca Malta and Crete

, Another use of a **comma** is to make a short pause inside a sentence. e.g. In spite of having a painful ankle, Rob continued the hill walk.

Put one comma in each sentence to make a pause.

1   After a long walk to the top of the hill   we sat down for a rest.
2   If you continue along that path and follow the signs   you will reach the little café.
3   Although it had been a long and tiring day   we felt satisfied with our efforts.
4   Before going to our comfortable bunks   we enjoyed a delicious meal.

Words which are actually **spoken** are written inside **inverted commas**.
e.g. Robin said, "I am going to Nottingham."

Underline the words in each sentence which are actually spoken.
Write each sentence with the spoken words in **inverted commas**.

1 When Robin saw the stranger he cried, Stand back!

....

2 Stand back yourself, was the reply.

....

3 Robin demanded, Do you want an arrow in your ribs?

....

4 The stranger laughed and said, Do you want my stick across your back?

....

....

When the speaker's name comes in the **middle** of the words spoken, the second
part of the sentence begins again with a small letter.
e.g. "My name," said the stranger, "is Will Scarlet."

Write each sentence with the spoken words in **inverted commas**.

1 Don't you know, boasted Robin, that I'm the strongest man in Sherwood?

....

....

2 Come on then, retorted Will, and show me what you can do.

....

3 If you want a fight, cried Robin, you can have it.

....

Write this paragraph in three sentences with the correct punctuation.

Robin held up his hand and
whispered we must lie low What
can you hear asked Will Scarlet
I think Robin replied that
someone is hiding in that tree

....

....

....

....

....

Standard English

Some nouns are **masculine gender**.	Some nouns are **feminine gender**.	Some nouns can be of **masculine** or **feminine gender**.
e.g. A **boy** is **male**.	e.g. A **girl** is **female**.	e.g. A **child** is of **common gender**.

Read the nouns in the box.

king	lord	uncle	father	wife
infant	duke	lady	cousin	daughter
grandparent	prince	nephew	husband	son
actor	baby	teenager	niece	princess
mother	actress	queen	duchess	aunt

Write each noun under the correct **gender** heading.

masculine		feminine		common

Change each noun of **feminine gender** to **masculine gender** and change each noun of **masculine gender** to **feminine gender**.

1   The queen was succeeded by the young princess.

2   The Duchess of Bath has a clever daughter.

3   My aunt's niece is coming to stay with us.

4   My father's mother is my grandmother.

5   Lady Derwent is the daughter of Lord Derby.

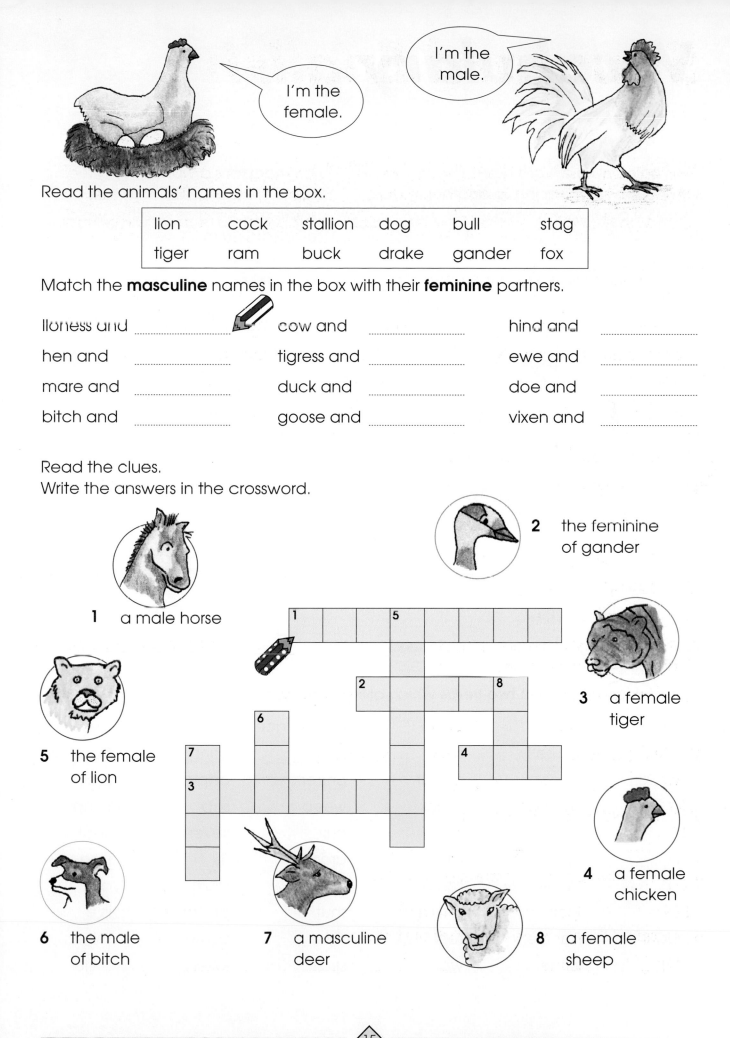

I'm the female.

I'm the male.

Read the animals' names in the box.

lion	cock	stallion	dog	bull	stag
tiger	ram	buck	drake	gander	fox

Match the **masculine** names in the box with their **feminine** partners.

lioness and ....   cow and ....   hind and ....

hen and ....   tigress and ....   ewe and ....

mare and ....   duck and ....   doe and ....

bitch and ....   goose and ....   vixen and ....

Read the clues.
Write the answers in the crossword.

1   a male horse

2   the feminine of gander

3   a female tiger

5   the female of lion

4   a female chicken

6   the male of bitch

7   a masculine deer

8   a female sheep

Vocabulary

An **antonym** is a word having the **opposite** meaning to another word.   e.g. lucky : unlucky

A **synonym** is a word having the **same** meaning, or nearly the same meaning as another word. e.g. hard : firm

Write the **antonyms**, using the correct prefix from each box.

| in / dis | correct _____ | im / il | patient _____ | un / il | lawful _____ |
| in / im | possible _____ | il / in | expensive _____ | in / dis | visible _____ |

Write the **antonym** which describes:

1   something which can't be seen _____

2   someone who is restless and can't wait _____

3   something in which there is a mistake _____

4   against the law _____

5   costing very little _____

6   something which can't be done _____

Draw (rings) round the **two verbs** which are **synonyms** of the verb in captial letters.

BEGIN	start	arrive	commence	use	rest
BREAK	bruise	snap	bribe	bring	fracture
CHOOSE	select	cheat	cheer	copy	pick
CRY	whisper	crack	weep	sob	cringe
CUT	cure	saw	curl	sever	knot
FALL	sink	faint	drop	fly	fling
HELP	hinder	hope	hold	assist	aid
KEEP	lock	retain	shut	preserve	live
TOUCH	handle	feel	save	polish	shine
WALK	stride	wait	stroll	loiter	linger

Which is which?

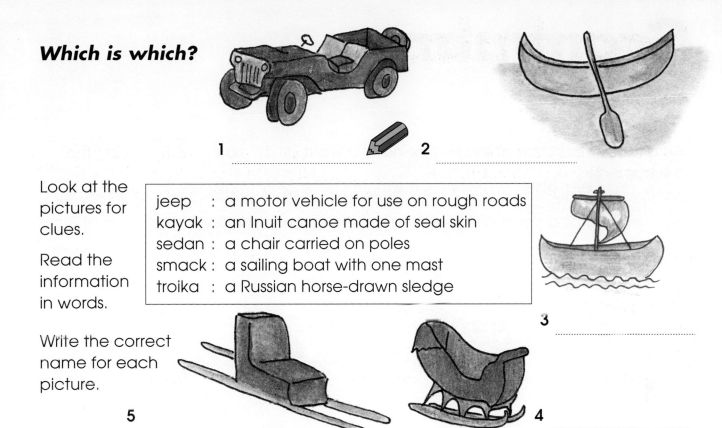

Look at the pictures for clues.

Read the information in words.

jeep	: a motor vehicle for use on rough roads
kayak	: an Inuit canoe made of seal skin
sedan	: a chair carried on poles
smack	: a sailing boat with one mast
troika	: a Russian horse-drawn sledge

Write the correct name for each picture.

1 _____   2 _____

3 _____

5 _____   4 _____

The clue to the missing word is the sentence itself.
Write the word from the box which makes the best sense. Read **all** the sentence.

1
atlas
diary
dictionary

I keep an account of what I do each day in my _____ .

2
maths
geography
history

I looked up Queen Victoria's dates in my _____ book.

3
satchel
handbag
sack

After supper I put my school books into my _____ .

4
group
bunch
team

I'm hoping to represent my school in the football _____ .

Challenge

Write **one** word which can mean:

loved
and
expensive _____

amusing
and
strange _____

is able
and
tin of food _____

Grammar

A **prefix** is an addition at the **beginning** of a word.

e.g. **dis**–   **dis**agree   **dis**trust

Give these words an **opposite** meaning by writing the prefix **dis**– in front of each one.

.... like   .... obey   .... honest

.... appear   .... order   .... pleased

Write the word from the list above which describes:

1   a feeling of not liking   ....

2   likely to lie, cheat or steal   ....

3   a mess or confusion   ....

4   to move out of sight   ....

5   to be annoyed   ....

6   to refuse to obey   ....

A **suffix** is an addition at the **end** of a word.

e.g. -**less**   harm**less**   noise**less**

Write the suffix -**less** at the end of each of these words.

use ....   care ....   cheer....................

pain ....   hope....................   joy....................

Underline the **adjective** in each sentence.
Write each sentence so that it has the **opposite** meaning by changing the **suffix**.

1   These scissors are useful.   1   ....

2   You're being careless!   2   ....

3   I began to feel hopeless.   3   ....

4   It was a cheerful scene.   4   ....

5   My hand is painless.   5   ....

6   What a joyless party!   6   ....

| A **noun** is a naming word. | An **adjective** describes a noun. | A **pronoun** stands for a noun. | A **verb** tells us what is being done. | A **preposition** shows the relationship between two nouns or pronouns. |

Colour the **one** word in each row which tells you the name of the **part of speech** which the other words belong to.

happy	adjectives	delighted	merry	elated
chair	table	nouns	bed	stool
hop	leap	jump	verbs	vault
between	prepositions	through	above	under
it	they	she	we	pronouns

Read these sentences:
Draw a (ring) round the nouns.
Draw a <u>line</u> under the adjectives.

Write the verbs here:

1   Happy children ran over the yellow sand.

2   Little crabs crawled round the rocky pools.

3   Two seagulls flew above the blue water.

4   The bright sun slipped behind fluffy clouds.

....

....

....

....

Write the four prepositions from the sentences above:

....

....

Draw a (ring) round each pronoun in these sentences:

1   The teacher said that she would read us a story.

2   Would you like to dance with me?

3   Bola and I held up the baton to show that we were ready.

4   Tom said that he would go if they went too.

5   We watched the tennis and they watched the cricket.

Comprehension

Read about **A Highwaywoman**

Moll Cutpurse was a highwaywoman whose real name was Mary Frith. When she was ten years old she began wearing men's clothes, learned to smoke a pipe, and picked the pockets of people as they walked along the busy streets of London. When she was fifteen she became a highwaywoman, riding her horse out of the city and robbing travellers as they rode to and from London.

Moll soon became rich and lived in style in a large house in Fleet Street. She opened a shop where she sold her stolen goods. It is said that she gave the owners the first chance of buying back their own stolen belongings.

One day she was arrested for galloping down Fleet Street dressed in men's clothes, blowing a trumpet and waving a flag. As a punishment she had to kneel at St Paul's Cross, wearing a white sheet to show that she was sorry for her sins.

Moll escaped being hanged for her many crimes and lived to the ripe old age of seventy-five.

Read the questions.

Draw a (ring) round the correct answer.

1 What was Moll Cutpurse's real name?

Mary Cutpurse   Moll Frith   Mary Frith

2 In which city did Moll live?

Bath   London   Chester

3 How old was Moll when she learned to smoke a pipe?

ten   fifteen   seventy-five

About the story

Read the questions.

Choose the best word, or group of words, to fit the information and put a (ring) round it.

1   What did Moll start wearing when she was ten years old?

long dresses   men's clothes   pretty hats

2   What did Moll start doing when she was fifteen years old?

going to church   working in a shop   robbing travellers

3   How was Moll punished for making a disturbance?

She knelt at St Paul's Cross in a white sheet.   She was sent to prison.   She was whipped.

How the story is written

Draw a (ring) round the best word for your answer.

1   The word **banner** means: bandit   flower   flag

2   The word **sorry** means: painful   remorseful   unpleasant

Write **one** sentence about Moll's shop and the goods she sold.

....

Using your best joined up handwriting, copy this sentence on the lines below.

The age of highway robbers lasted about two hundred years, between A.D.1600 and A.D.1800.

....

....

....

Spelling

Draw a (ring) round **gu** in these words.

guard	guarantee	guess	guest	guide
guilty	guinea pig	guillotine	guitar	guild

Write the words from the box that have the following meanings:

1 .... a musical instrument

2 .... an instrument for cutting paper

3 .... someone paying a visit to someone else's house

4 .... a person or thing that shows the way

5 .... to protect someone or something

6 .... to be responsible for doing something wrong

Use your dictionary to check your answers.

Draw a (ring) round the words which are a **synonym** of the word in capital letters.

The **–ant** family

1 PLEASANT
- agreeable
- a country person
- a game bird

2 IGNORANT
- taking no notice
- having little knowledge
- going away

3 INFANT
- beforehand
- to pretend
- a young child

4 DISTANT
- easily seen
- far away
- to twist

The **–ent** family

1 EXPERIMENT
- a journey
- a test or try-out
- to put on show

2 ARGUMENT
- a quarrel in words
- a covered walk
- hard and difficult

3 FRAGMENT
- very weak
- a broken bone
- a small piece

4 FREQUENT
- wild excitement
- happening often
- new or different

Read about **Musical Instruments**

Some musical instruments, such as the harp and guitar, have strings, played with the fingers, to make sounds. The violin has strings, but is played with a bow. The sound of the pipe is made by the player opening and closing holes with his or her fingers. A trumpet's sound is produced by vibrating air with the lips, inside the instrument. Percussion instruments, like tambourines, drums and cymbals make their sound when they are shaken, hit or struck together.

Look carefully at the names of the instuments and then cover over the paragraph.

LOOK	SAY	COVER	WRITE	CHECK
at each word	each word	each word	from memory	your spelling

drum
harp
violin
trumpet
pipe
tambourine
guitar
cymbals

Challenge

Write the names of the musical instruments from these pictograms (picture words).

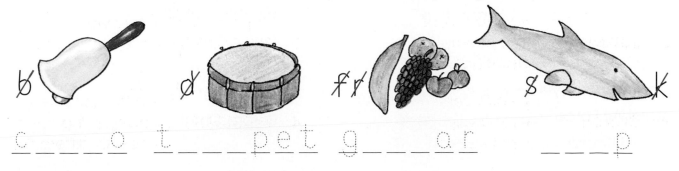

c _ _ _ o   t _ _ pet   g _ _ _ ar   _ _ _ p

Standard English

An **abbreviation** is a short way of writing a word.

e.g. **St.** for Street   **P.O.** for Post Office

Write the names of these abbreviations for parts of speech. (Use page 19 to help you.)

n. ....   pron. ....   adj. ....

v. ....   prep. ....

These phrases can be used in writing:

p.t.o.	means	please turn over
e.g.	means	for example
p.s.	means	postscript . . . written later
etc.	means	et cetera . . . and so on

Write sentences of your own choice, to describe where you might use these abbreviations.

....

....

....

....

....

....

....

Abbreviations are often made using the initial letters of proper nouns.

e.g. **S.O.S.** for **S**ave **O**ur **S**ouls.

Write abbreviations, using initial letters for:

British Broadcasting Corporation ....   Victoria Cross ....

Royal Society (for the) Prevention
(of) Cruelty (to) Animals ....   Police Constable ....

On Her Majesty's Service ....   Her Majesty's Ship ....

Royal Air Force ....   Justice (of the) Peace ....

United Kingdom ....   Before Christ ....

The points of the compass indicate direction:

north
south
east
west

Write these directions **in full**:

NE _northeast_   SW _____

S _____   E _____

NW _____   SE _____

N _____   W _____

The names of many counties are abbreviated.
Join these abbreviations with their full names.

Bucks.	Nottinghamshire	Yorks.	Staffordshire
Oxon.	Buckinghamshire	Hants.	Lancashire
Notts.	Bedfordshire	Wilts.	Yorkshire
Glos.	Oxfordshire	Lancs.	Wiltshire
Beds.	Gloucestershire	Staffs.	Hampshire

In which school subject might you use these weights and measures?

litre   gramme   metre

millilitre   kilogramme   kilometre

....

Write the abbreviations in full:

40 ml   150 g   1 kg   2 m   20 km

millilitres   _____   _____   _____

Challenge Write | yes | or | no | in answer to these questions:

1   You can park on Tues. between 11a.m. and 1p.m.

2   You can park on Thurs. between 9 p.m. and 11p.m.

3   You can park on Sun. between 1a.m. and 5 p.m.

4   You can park on Fri. between 7a.m. and 10 a.m.

NO PARKING
Mon. - Sat.
8a.m. - 6p.m.

Making notes

Read each sentence.
Cross out the words which are **not** important to the meaning.

Write the four **key words** from each sentence in the notebook.

1   Both a square and a rectangle have four sides.

2   The distance round a square is called the perimeter.

3   Some measurements are metres, centimetres and millimetres.

4   Circles, cubes and cones are all shapes.

5   A football and a bicycle wheel are both circular.

6   A diagram is a plan made to explain or illustrate something.

1
2
3
4
5
6

Read each set of **notes**.

Write a complete sentence for each set.

quadrilaterals
polygons   octagons
geometric shapes

1

line
diameter   circle
side   passing   centre

2

radius
line   centre   straight
circumference

3

Write the five **key words** from each sentence in the notebook.

1   The brain, the heart and the lungs are all organs of the body.

2   The heart pumps blood round the body.

3   The brain is protected by a bony framework called the skull.

4   The lungs are a pair of organs for breathing air.

Write the **key words** for each sentence as notes.

1   Fuel is a material which is burnt to provide us with heat or power.

2   Electricity is a power used for lighting, heating and working machinery.

3   Coal, wood and oil are all substances which can give heat or power.

Read each paragraph.

A magnet is a piece of metal which has the power of attracting pieces of iron. For example, it can pull a paper clip along a piece of paper.

A steel drum is a musical intrument from Trinidad. It is made from a large oil drum. Notes are made by hitting the top with a beater.

Write useful notes here:

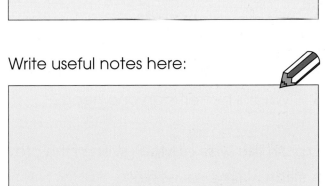

Vocabulary

A **proverb** is a short, well-known saying which gives **wise** advice.

Read these proverbs. Write a proverb, from the list, under each picture.

Slow and steady wins the race.	Every cloud has a silver lining.
Two heads are better than one.	The early bird catches the worm.
Too many cooks spoil the broth.	

Answer these questions:

1   What has every cloud got?

2   What spoils the broth?

3   What does the early bird catch?

4   What kind of effort wins the race?

5   What's better than one head?

Explain the wise advice given in this proverb:

A stitch in time saves nine.

Using your best joined up handwriting, copy these proverbs:

He who hesitates is lost.

Look before you leap.

Some of our **traditional sayings** express something in an **unusual** way.

e.g. Another way of saying, "I'm very pleased" is to say, "I'm over the moon".

Match each **saying** to its meaning:

1	to get into hot water	to make a fresh start
2	to let the cat out of the bag	to be ashamed of yourself
3	to hang one's head	to be sad
4	to blow your own trumpet	to get into trouble
5	to be down in the dumps	to boast
6	to turn over a new leaf	to give away a secret

Write six sentences of your own using each of the **sayings**.

....

....

....

....

....

Explain each of these sayings:

It's raining <u>cats and dogs</u>.

....

He gave me <u>the lion's share</u>.

....

She behaved like <u>a bull in a china shop</u>.

....

When I was wrong I had <u>to eat my own words</u>.

....

We did not have a happy holiday because my sister was <u>a wet blanket</u>.

....

Test your progress

Write each set of words in **alphabetical order**.

index	prefix	verb
atlas	opposite	preposition
library	abbreviation	adjective
dictionary	synonym	pronoun

Underline the nouns and put a (ring) round the prepositions in each sentence.

1   The train went under the bridge and through the tunnel.

2   John sat against the bench beneath the tree.

3   The dog was inside the kennel and the cat was in the basket.

4   The postman went up the path and put the letters into the box.

Put the correct punctuation in each balloon.

1   What a good idea ◯ exclaimed the teacher ◯

2   If you still have a pain tomorrow ◯ you must go to the doctor ◯

3   Beans ◯ carrots ◯ potatoes and onions are all vegetables ◯

Complete these words with the correct spelling.

1   _ _ _ a n g l e
a percussion instrument

2   d e l _ _ _ e d
very pleased

3   _ _ m p o r t _ _ _
not to be treated seriously

4   b a l _ _ _ _
to make a thing steady

5   p i _ _ _ _
to put up a tent

6   m e s s _ _ _
a note sent to someone

7   _ _ a r a n t _ _
to make a solemn promise

8   d i s _ _ _ _
far away

Colour in how many you got right on the ladder and
your mistakes on the snake.

30

Give these words the opposite meaning by writing **dis**– in front of each one.

appear ....   like ....

believe ....   comfort ....

advantage ....

Write abbreviations for the following:

National Society for the Prevention of Cruelty to Children ....

People's Dispensary for Sick Animals ....   Royal Navy ....

southwest ....   State Registered Nurse ....

Underline the masculine gender nouns and put a (ring) round the feminine gender nouns in each sentence.

1   The old lady was taken home by the policeman.

2   My mother has one niece and two nephews.

3   The postman had a letter for John and a postcard for Jane.

4   In the farmyard were a ram, a mare and a goose.

5   The dog chased the hen and the bull charged at the man.

Underline the adjective and draw a (ring) round the two pronouns in each sentence.

1   The clever carpenter said that he would soon repair it.

2   Jane said that she would like me to visit the old lady.

3   You said that they were guilty of a serious crime.

4   John had a bright idea and we all agreed to it.

5   Peter and I asked little Tom to come with us.

Draw (rings) round the two words which are synonyms of the word in capital letters.

ROUGH	long	uneven	straight	bumpy	full
BRAVE	happy	courageous	peaceful	sensible	bold
HIGH	thin	famous	lofty	pointed	tall
BEAUTIFUL	straight	strange	fine	lovely	famous
SAD	glum	tired	joyless	patient	happy

Colour in how many you got right on the ladder and your mistakes on the snake.

31

Answers

page 2

B C D E F G H I J K L M N O P Q R S T U V W X Y

search	gaze	pace
skate	glare	plod
swing	grasp	prowl
wrap	spell	kneel
wreck	splendid	know
write	spring	knuckle

1 quantity   2 quartet
3 question   4 queue

page 3

ruler   square   oblong   rectangle
do not write in my book

page 4

1 in Westminster Abbey   2 nine
3 the Lord Protector

page 5

1 because Edward was so young
2 Prison Bars   3 of a chill

1 to keep safe   2 to rule

Barnaby was important to Edward because if ever the king did anything wrong, Barnaby was punished instead.

page 6

past, through, round, over, by

page 7

below and above	with and without
to and from	on and off
before and after	outside and inside
down and up	

1 The cat ran **outside** the shed.
2 A tram went **under** the bridge.
3 My friend went **before** me.
4 I forgot to turn **off** the light.
5 Birds flew **above** the trees.

1 hunter, bushes	through
2 soldier, tank	behind
3 fish, surface	beneath
4 Ahmet, ball, wall	against
5 Sukie, apples, basket	into
6 child, wall	off

page 8

garage	balance	uniform	trio
message	lance	united	tripod
average	entrance	unicorn	triangle
manage	distance	universe	triplet

page 9

1 There are eleven players in a football **team**.
2 The juicy **peach** was quite delicious.
3 The **stream** ran into a wide river.
4 I put butter and jam on my **bread**.
5 We laid the **table** ready for supper.
6 Our best **plate** crashed to the floor.

page 10

1 penguins, live, Antarctic
2 whales, live, sea
3 flying-fish, glide, fins
4 mosquitoes, carry, diseases
5 greenfly, common, insect
6 snakes, crawl, ground
7 spider, eight, legs
8 bat, winged, mammal

For example:
1 Bees collect pollen to make honey.
2 Robins, sparrows and pigeons all have wings.
3 A tortoise's eggs are the size of tennis balls.

page 11

1 monkeys, apes, humans, primates
2 lizard, replace, lost, tail
3 lion, tiger, leopard, carnivorous
4 insects, birds, migrate, swarms
5 wolves, foxes, family, dogs
6 kangaroo, keeps, young, pouch

1 A giraffe uses its long neck to reach leaves high up in trees.
2 Eagles' claws are good for seizing prey.
3 A squirrel makes its nest, called a drey, in a tree.

page 12

1 ?	2 !	3 ?	4 .	5 !
6 ?	7 .	8 !	9 ?	10 !

1 The Cam, Dee, Ure and Wye are all English rivers.
2 Some capital cities of Europe are Paris, Rome, Oslo, London and Berlin.
3 Ayr, Alva and Elie are Scottish towns.
4 In the Mediterranean are the islands of Majorca, Malta and Crete.

1 After a long walk to the top of the hill, we sat down for a rest.
2 If you continue along that path and follow the signs, you will reach the little café.
3 Although it had been a long and tiring day, we felt satisfied with our efforts.
4 Before going to our comfortable bunks, we enjoyed a delicious meal.

page 13

1 When Robin saw the stranger he cried, "<u>Stand back!</u>"
2 "<u>Stand back yourself</u>," was the reply.
3 Robin demanded, "<u>Do you want an arrow in your ribs</u>?"
4 The stranger laughed and said, "<u>Do you want my stick across your back</u>?"

1 "Don't you know," boasted Robin, "that I'm the strongest man in Sherwood?"
2 "Come on then," retorted Will, "and show me what you can do."
3 "If you want a fight," cried Robin, "you can have it."

page 13 continued

Robin held up his hand and whispered, "We must lie low."
"What can you hear?" asked Will Scarlet.
"I think," Robin replied, "that someone is hiding in that tree."

page 14

masculine king uncle actor nephew lord son duke father prince husband
feminine mother duchess actress wife lady daughte queen princess niece aunt
common infant grandparent baby teenager cousin

1 The king was succeeded by the young prince.
2 The Duke of Bath has a clever son.
3 My uncle's nephew is coming to stay with us.
4 My mother's father is my grandfather.
5 Lord Derwent is the son of Lady Derby.

page 15

lion	bull	stag
cock	tiger	ram
stallion	drake	buck
dog	gander	fox

1 stallion	2 goose	3 tigress	4 hen
5 lioness	6 dog	7 stag	8 ewe

page 16

incorrect	**im**patient	**un**lawful
impossible	**in**expensive	**in**visible

1 invisible   2 impatient   3 incorrect
4 unlawful   5 inexpensive   6 impossible

BEGIN	start, commence
BREAK	snap, fracture
CHOOSE	select, pick
CRY	weep, sob
CUT	saw, sever
FALL	sink, drop
HELP	assist, aid
KEEP	retain, preserve
TOUCH	handle, feel
WALK	stride, stroll

page 17

1 jeep   2 kayak   3 smack   4 troika
5 sedan

1 diary   2 history   3 satchel   4 team
dear   funny   can

page 18

1 dislike   2 dishonest   3 disorder
4 disappear   5 displeased   6 disobey

1	useful	These scissors are **useless**.
2	careless	You're being **careful**!
3	hopeless	I began to feel **hopeful**.
4	cheerful	It was a **cheerless** scene.
5	painless	My hand is **painful**.
6	joyless	What a **joyful** party!